Grammar, Punctuation & Spelling Activity Book

for ages 10-11

This CGP book is bursting with fun activities to build up children's skills and confidence.

It's ideal for extra practice to reinforce what they're learning in primary school. Enjoy!

Published by CGP

Editors:
Keith Blackhall, Emma Cleasby, Rachel Craig-McFeely,
Alex Fairer, Becca Lakin and Katya Parkes

With thanks to Harriet Foster and Catherine Heygate for the proofreading.

With thanks to Lottie Edwards for the copyright research.

ISBN: 978 1 78908 738 3

Printed by Elanders Ltd, Newcastle upon Tyne.
Clipart on the cover and throughout the book from Corel®
Cover design concept by emc design ltd.

Contents

Tenses

How It Works

The tense or form of a verb tells you when something happened.

The present progressive form shows an action is happening now.

The shark is eating a small fish. ← You use the present tense form of 'to be' and a verb with 'ing'.

The past progressive form shows an action was happening in the past.

The shark was eating a small fish. ← You use the past tense form of 'to be' and a verb with 'ing'.

The present perfect form is used to talk about things that happened recently.

They have found the missing cat. ← You use the present tense of 'to have' and a verb in the past tense.

The past perfect form is used to talk about things that happened before something else.

They had found the missing cat. ← You use the past tense of 'to have' and a verb in the past tense.

Now Try These

1. Circle the right form of the verb to complete each sentence.
   Then, draw lines to show which form each sentence uses.

   We **was** / **were** wondering who her hairdresser was.   present progressive

   I **has** / **have** written a thrilling story about a snail.   past progressive

   The car journey **had** / **were** been long and tiring.   present perfect

   Jemima **is** / **are** riding her horse called Matilda.   past perfect

2. Complete each sentence using a verb from the box. Match each verb to the form in brackets.

   Leila _is giving_ **(present perfect)** cards to her friends.

   The explorers _sailed_ **(past perfect)** across the ocean.

   Evan _did maintain_ **(present progressive)** to the zoo keeper.

   I _danced_ **(past progressive)** around the room with joy.

   | to give |
   | to talk |
   | to sail |
   | to dance |

3. Rewrite each sentence so that it uses the form in brackets.

Sonja hopes to become a pirate. **(past perfect)**

Sonja had hoped to become a pirate.

The superhero flew around the rooftops. **(past progressive)**

The superhero was ~~flyed~~ flying around ~~the~~ rooftops. ✓

They uncovered an ancient city beneath the sand. **(present progressive)**

The ~~are~~ found an ancient city beneath the sand.

The magician lifts the table with a spell. **(present perfect)**

The magician ~~was~~ lifting the ~~tabl~~ table with a spell.

4. Write one present progressive sentence and one past perfect sentence.
Use both of the words in the box in each sentence.

chicken
bicycle

Present progressive: The chicen is riding a horse. ✓

Past perfect: The bicycle was broken.

An Extra Challenge

Jamal has written a diary entry for his English homework, but his naughty brother Gatik has changed the tenses as a prank. Can you underline the verbs that are written incorrectly? ⭐

Then, rewrite Jamal's diary entry so that each verb uses the right tense.

Dear Diary,
Today, while my brothers was browsing the bookshop, I was tried on clothes at the new shop in town. I had want to visit since it opened. I noticed that the shop is selling a variety of fancy, blue suits. I have dreaming of owning such a suit for a long time, so I was thinking of buying one. When I am showing off my new suit to my friends later on, they admired my trendy new look.

Did these tenses sharpen your senses? Tick a box.

Noun phrases

How It Works

A phrase is usually a group of words that doesn't contain a verb.
A noun phrase contains a noun and any words that describe that noun.

the superhero ← This is a noun phrase, but it doesn't give you much information.

Noun phrases can be expanded by adding extra adjectives, prepositions and nouns. This is an expanded noun phrase:

the amazing **superhero** in a flowing green cape on top of the mountain

| adjective | preposition | adjectives | noun | preposition | noun |

Now Try These

1. Fill in the gap in each sentence with either a noun, an adjective or a preposition to complete the noun phrase.

He finally spotted the ....._Rocky_..... coastline of the small island.

Vinodh asked the tall, ..._hairy_..... man behind the counter a question.

She lives in a strange, futuristic house ....._~~next~~ around_..... the town centre.

I donated an enormous stack of ....._Clothes_..... to the charity shop.

2. Write an expanded noun phrase that contains the words in each box.

| boy annoying nearby funfair | → | There was a ~~scel~~ annoying boy nearby the funfair. |

| ~~mole~~ friendly sandy beach | → | There was a fat mole eating a friendly pop ice lolly on a sandy beech. |

4

3. Underline the longest noun phrase in each sentence below, then write a replacement noun phrase that would still make sense in the sentence.

Will and his entire family visited the adorable baby elephants at the zoo.

....

I gave a glass of freshly-squeezed orange juice to my younger sister Ellie.

....

4. Rewrite each sentence below, expanding the underlined noun phrases by adding extra words before and after the nouns.

The toddler cuddled her dog and a cat.

....

....

The chef made a meal in his kitchen.

....

....

An Extra Challenge

Can you write some expanded noun phrases about the objects that you can see around you? Write five expanded noun phrases, and include words before and after the noun.

Use these prompts to help you think about how to describe the objects in your noun phrases.

| Where is it located? | What is its texture like? | How heavy is it? |

| What shape and size is it? | What colour is it? |

| What other adjectives could you use to describe it? |

Has your noun phrase know-how expanded? Give a box a tick.

Clauses

A main clause makes sense on its own. A subordinate clause gives extra information, but it doesn't make sense on its own.

He realised he was overdressed when he arrived at the pool.

 main clause   subordinate clause

Subordinate clauses can come before or after the main clause.

A relative clause is a type of subordinate clause. They are often introduced by relative pronouns (such as who, which and that) and give extra information about a noun.

We know somebody (who) is really good at fixing cars.

     relative pronoun   relative clause

Sometimes, the relative pronoun can be left out of the relative clause and the sentence will still make sense.

Now Try These

1. Tick the sentences that contain a relative clause, then underline the relative clauses.

    Everyone here is in fancy dress except Holly and Ichika. ☐

    The milk in the tea that I'm drinking doesn't taste fresh. ☐

    Harper tried to find out who had dressed up the dog. ☐

    That summer we spent surfing at the beach was fun. ☐

2. Complete the sentences below by adding a relative clause.

John, ... , explored the ruins.

We opened the door, ... , and peeked inside.

My house is on a hill ....

I looked at the sky ....

Lucy, ... , wanted a haircut.

3. Rewrite each sentence below so that it contains a subordinate clause.
   Use the conjunction in brackets to start the subordinate clause.

   I rode my bike to school. **(because)**

   ....

   The spell won't work. **(unless)**

   ....

   We can go jet-skiing. **(once)**

   ....

4. Use the words in each box below to write a sentence
   that contains a main clause and a relative clause.

   | band excited whose | ➡ | .... |

   ....

   | lightning bright that | ➡ | .... |

   ....

An Extra Challenge

Oh no! Tomasz has written a note about what he did yesterday, but his hamster has
ripped it into pieces. Can you rewrite the note by putting the pieces in the right order?
Then, count the number of main clauses in the note.

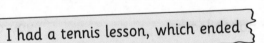

some cake, which

I had a tennis lesson, which ended

we were exhausted. Then we ate

so hard his racket broke!

had a water fight.   to cool off, we   I hit the ball   We played until

we felt was well deserved. In order   in a match with Fred.

**Are your answers clauses for
celebration? Give a box a tick.**

Conjunctions

How It Works

Co-ordinating conjunctions join two main clauses together.

I enjoy reading books but I love playing football.

first main clause   co-ordinating conjunction   second main clause

These words are all co-ordinating conjunctions:

For And Nor But Or Yet So ← Use FANBOYS to help you remember these co-ordinating conjunctions.

Subordinating conjunctions join a subordinate clause to a main clause. They can go at the start or in the middle of a sentence.

Jane was annoyed (since) Simon wouldn't keep the noise down.

main clause   subordinating conjunction   subordinate clause

Now Try These

1. Use the conjunctions from the box below to complete the sentences.

though	for	until	whenever	provided that

.... Danny sees a tree, he can't resist climbing it.

George thanked them many times, ... he was extremely grateful.

.... there are enough seats on the spaceship, you can all come along.

We promise not to leave .... you are ready.

.... the cheese is delicious, I won't have any more.

2. Underline the conjunction in each sentence, then tick the sentences that contain a subordinating conjunction.

I couldn't hear her since the music was too loud.

Stan loves cheddar but he won't eat brie.

I screamed when I saw my haircut.

Divya's very fast so she won.

☐   ☐   ☐   ☐

3. Can you join each group of sentences together using conjunctions?
   Use two different conjunctions in each of your new sentences.

   We were lost. I had followed the directions. I looked at the map again.

   ....

   ....

   Alice bought some paint. She planned to decorate. She moved house.

   ....

   ....

4. Use a subordinating conjunction to join each pair of sentences together so that the
   sentence in red is a main clause and the sentence in blue becomes a subordinate clause.

   He's been learning karate. He was a young boy.

   ....

   They can't open the chest. They find the key.

   ....

   It wasn't allowed. Kyle stood on the chair.

   ....

An Extra Challenge

Imagine you're eating in the cafe below. Write as many sentences as you can to describe what's happening, using at least one conjunction in each sentence. Try to use a variety of conjunctions.

Can you use conjunctions
without confusion? Tick a box.

9

Adverbials

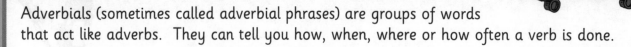

How It Works

Adverbials (sometimes called adverbial phrases) are groups of words that act like adverbs. They can tell you how, when, where or how often a verb is done.

This shows how the verb happens.   This shows when the verb happens.

Sally grinned with enthusiasm. She loved skating after school.

She fell over in the skate park — she falls over every time!

This shows where the verb happens.   This shows how often the verb happens.

Now Try These

1. Use the adverbials in the box to fill the gaps below. You should only use each option once.

in contrast	every so often	very quietly

.... , I buy sweets with my pocket money.

Karim likes potatoes. .... , I despise them.

The teacher told us we had to sit ....

2. Underline the adverbial in each sentence below. Then write down whether the adverbial is describing '**how**', '**when**', '**where**' or '**how often**' the verb is done.

We decided to go home as soon as possible. ....

Josie practises the guitar once or twice a day. ....

With extreme caution, Pandora lifted the lid. ....

I think that I left my homework on the bus. ....

3. Fill in the table, adding a different adverbial to each sentence to provide the information given in each column heading. The first one has been done for you.

	when	where	how	how often
I run.	I run after school.			
Elsa shouted.				

4. Can you replace the adverb in each sentence below with an adverbial? Make sure the adverbial gives the same extra information as the adverb.

My cousins live nearby.

....

They sleep through their alarms often.

....

Frantically, Ahmed looked for his keys.

....

An Extra Challenge

Can you describe what is happening in each image below? Make sure you use adverbials to show where, when and how each event is happening.

Did you complete this page <u>very quickly</u>, <u>with ease</u>? Tick a box.

11

Subject and object

How It Works

The subject of a sentence is the person or thing doing the verb. It usually comes first in a sentence.

The object of a sentence has the verb done to it. It usually comes after the verb.

Raouf sings a song.

↑ subject ↑ verb ↑ object

Harry dropped Alexis.

↑ subject ↑ verb ↑ object

Now Try These

1. Underline the subject and circle the object in each sentence below.

    The cat lapped up the cream.

    Bert smashed the precious vase.

    The policeman helped her.

    I accidentally squashed the grape.

    The friendly robot raised her arm.

    Paul swallowed the sweet whole.

    Noah hugged his pet duck gently.

    My teacher told me off angrily.

2. Complete each sentence below with the right word or phrase from the box.
    Then, label the word or phrase you've added as '**subject**', '**verb**' or '**object**'.

    Dom .... the rabbit. ➡ ....

    .... stamped its hoof. ➡ ....

    .... chewed the bone. ➡ ....

    | the dog |
    | emailed |
    | the unicorn |
    | stroked |
    | his basket |

    Hiro emptied .... ➡ ....

    She .... her aunt. ➡ ....

3. Complete each sentence by writing a subject or object in the gap.

subject .... lay down on the double bed.

object Horace bought .... for his garden.

object The gigantic dinosaur chased ....

subject .... stood in front of the class and sighed.

object With great care, Professor Lindal lifted up ....

4. Can you write a sentence to describe each of the pictures below?
   Then, underline the subject and circle the object you have used in each sentence.

....

....

....

....

....

....

An Extra Challenge

Can you write five sentences using each of the subjects and verbs below once?
You'll need to add you own object to each sentence.

| ate | Chidima | scared | the brave mouse |

| | greeted | the chickens | heaved |

| | Raphaelle | painted | the shy child |

Now, label the subject, verb and object in each of the sentences you have written.

Do you object to ticking one of these boxes? Hopefully not!

13

Passive and active

In active sentences, the subject of the sentence does something to the object.

The zebra painted the picture.

↑ subject   ↑ verb   ↑ object

In passive sentences, something is done to the subject.

The picture **was painted** by the zebra.

↑ subject

The word by can introduce who does the action.

Now Try These

1. Draw lines to show whether each sentence is active (**A**) or passive (**P**).

> My brother played video games all afternoon.

> Clarisse was chased by a swarm of angry bees.

> The gold medals were awarded by the judges.

> The plant doubled in size within a single week.

> The party was organised by Patrick's mother.

2. Tick the sentences that are passive, then rewrite them as active sentences.

The goal was scored by Carlos. ☐   The bird flew away from Lucas. ☐

I enjoy walking by the seaside. ☐   The card was made by my aunt. ☐

....

....

3. Rewrite each sentence below, changing it from active to passive.

The hippo scared the flamingo.

....

Riya smashed my favourite mug.

....

The storm blew the tree over.

....

4. Put a tick in the box next to the passive sentences below. Then, label the underlined part of each sentence as either '**subject**' or '**object**'.

Obasi held the red ball. □ ➡ ....

Mia was given a kitten. □ ➡ ....

My mum won <u>the quiz</u>. □ ➡ ....

<u>The cake</u> was baked. □ ➡ ....

An Extra Challenge

Lola has written a story, using lots of passive sentences.

Can you rewrite the story so that all the sentences are active? Watch out, you might need to add more punctuation.

Doug and Kat were given their top secret mission by the head of Space Pets, Colonel Kitten. First, they were asked to locate the wicked alien by the Colonel. Then, they were instructed by him to send the alien back to its home planet.

"What if we are overpowered and the galaxy is conquered by evil forces?" Kat asked — she was alarmed by the scale of the mission. However, she was reassured by Doug.

"We were awarded the top prize by Space Pets last year. We can do this," he barked. "Let's go!" And so their jet packs were fired up and the top secret mission was started.

Did these pages activate your passive skills? Tick a box.

 □   □   □

15

Formal and informal writing

Formal writing is used for serious or important texts.
Informal writing is more chatty and friendly.

Formal and informal writing use different vocabulary.

The book was wonderful. ← formal vocabulary   **Ian** wound me up. ← informal vocabulary

Formal writing sometimes uses the subjunctive form.

Had I asked, he would have agreed. ← This is more formal than 'If I had asked'.

Were I to steal the jewels, I would not be caught. ← This is more formal than 'If I stole the jewels'.

Informal writing can use contractions. Adding questions to the end of statements is also a feature of informal writing.

He'll love it. ← You can say He'll instead of He will.   **It's ace,** isn't it?

Now Try These

1. Draw lines to join each informal sentence with the matching formal one.

| The chippy's brill, isn't it? | | If I were so inclined, I could have left. |

| I hang out with my mates. | | The chip shop is brilliant. |

| If I'd wanted to, I could've left. | | I spend time with my friends. |

2. For each sentence below, write **F** in the box if it is formal and **I** if it is informal.
   Then, underline the word or phrase that makes each sentence formal or informal.

The kids were playing inside. ☐   Max requested to leave the room. ☐

Jan ditched me outside the zoo. ☐   It was really enjoyable, wasn't it? ☐

I informed her about the test. ☐   Had I gone, I would have had fun. ☐

3. Use the words from the box below to complete these formal and informal sentences. Make sure the word fits the style of writing used in the rest of the sentence.

| chuffed | elated | busted | apprehended |

Catherine was dead .... about winning the race, wasn't she?

Khushi was .... when her dad saw her munching the sweets.

Were she to do something wrong, she would be ....

I was extremely .... about the outcome of the experiment.

4. Write **F** next to the formal sentences and **I** next to the informal sentences. Then rewrite the informal sentences to make them formal, and the formal sentences to make them informal.

Hand me the grub — I'm starving! ☐

....

My mother instructed Zara to relax. ☐

....

If I'd made a joke, she would've cracked up. ☐

....

An Extra Challenge

Kim has written a note to her dad and a letter of complaint, but she's used the wrong style of writing in both. Can you rewrite the texts so their level of formality matches their purpose?

Dear Father,
I have inquired with mother as to whether I am able to visit Tina's residence this evening, to which she responded 'yes'. Therefore, I will be absent from our evening meal tonight.

I'm pretty miffed about the bike I got from your shop. It's super grubby and the brakes are messed up. I'm normally not that fussed with complaining about stuff, but this has really got on my nerves because it was pretty pricey. Can you give me my money back? Ta.

Were these pages fab or fabulous? Give a box a tick.

Quizzical quest

Ribbit!

Oh no! You have been turned into a frog by a wicked witch. To turn yourself back into a human, you need to answer the following questions correctly. Next to each answer option is a letter — write the correct letters in the boxes on the next page to find out the magic word that will break the witch's spell.

1. Is this sentence active or passive?

The dog was given large, feathery wings by a fairy.

active — **S**   passive — **A**

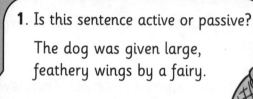

2. Is this sentence formal or informal?

There's something about that elf that's really bugging me.

formal — **H**   informal — **L**

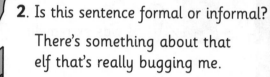

3. How many apostrophes are missing from this sentence?

Its furious that it cant breathe fire like its enemies can.

0 — **L**   2 — **A**

1 — **D**   3 — **F**

4. Who is doing the verb in an active sentence?

antonym — **G**   subject — **C**

object — **I**   clause — **P**

5. Which form is used in this sentence?

The witch has cast an evil curse on you.

present perfect — **K**   past perfect — **J**

present progressive — **H**   past progressive — **M**

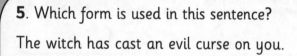

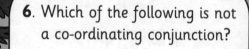

6. Which of the following is not a co-ordinating conjunction?

yet — **O**   but — **W**

nor — **U**   since — **A**

7. Which of the following is a synonym of '**wealthy**'?

miserly — **X**   affluent — **Z**

generous — **I**   destitute — **Q**

8. Does the sentence below use colons correctly?

I'm extremely skilled: at magic I practise every day.

yes — **E**   no — **A**

10. Which of the following is an adverbial in the sentence below?

The silly goblin danced all through the night.

danced — **E**   the silly goblin — **R**

all through the night — **O**

9. Which of the following is an antonym of '**repair**'?

destruction — **L**   disturb — **S**

renovate — **H**   demolish — **M**

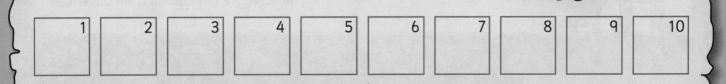

The magic word is...

1	2	3	4	5	6	7	8	9	10

Phew — you're no longer a frog! However, you still need to escape the witch's lair. Find the safe path across the booby-trapped floor by stepping on the words that are spelt correctly. You cannot move diagonally. Good luck!

START	cought	plausible	yacht	private	modeify
	suficient	conscience	differring	ghastly	harass
fascinate	horrorify	compromise	temperature	vareity	fourty
persuade	suspicious	onestly	sought	advize	appreceate
nominnate	caffeine	cemetry	mortify	potencial	solemn
prayse	programme	emergency	controversy	instrumant	brort

Synonyms and antonyms

How It Works

Synonyms are words that have the same or a very similar meaning.

↓

neat **and** tidy

Antonyms are words that mean the opposite of each other.

↓

start **and** finish

Synonyms and antonyms are always the same word type as each other.

✓ vivid **and** bright → These are synonyms — they're both adjectives that mean vibrant.

✗ swift **and** quickly → These are not synonyms — swift is an adjective but quickly is an adverb.

Now Try These

1. Draw lines to match each sentence to a synonym of the word in bold.

There was a moment of **quiet** before the storm hit.		stealthily
He **softly** stroked the puppy behind its ears.		peace
There was a brief **pause** in the conversation.		lull
The lizard moved **sneakily** across the glass.		gently

2. Label the underlined words in the sentences below with their word types. Then write an antonym for each word you've labelled in the box.

He <u>always</u> plays <u>harmless</u> pranks on his <u>enemy</u>.

↑   ↑   ↑

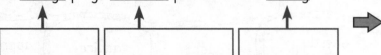

➡

His parents <u>punished</u> him for being <u>mean</u> to his sister.

↑   ↑

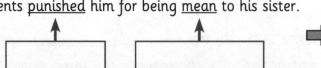

➡

3. Complete each sentence by writing a synonym of the word in brackets on the dotted lines.

Her .... attitude brightened my day. ➡ (cheerful)

I'm grateful to my friends for .... me. ➡ (assisting)

The antique necklace was very .... ➡ (beautiful)

They .... on baking the pie for dinner. ➡ (focused)

4. Rewrite each sentence, replacing the words in bold with antonyms so that each sentence means the opposite.

Emeka **loosely** wrapped himself up in the **coarse** blanket.

....

In **summer**, the nights are **shorter** and the days are **warmer**.

....

She **rejected** the invitation because it sounded **boring**.

....

Everybody was happy about the mission's **success**.

....

An Extra Challenge

Can you fill in the grid on the right with synonyms of the words in the boxes?

Unscramble the shaded letters to reveal a word that means 'lessen'.
Then write a sentence that uses an antonym of this word.

often ➡	f		e	q		e				y
laugh ➡		h	u	c			e			
coax ➡	p		r	s			d			
weak ➡	f	r			l					
surely ➡	c		r	t			n			
rage ➡	a		g							
shyly ➡	t		m	i			y			

Were these pages amazing or astonishing? Give a box a tick.

21

Apostrophes

How It Works

Apostrophes can be used to show where letters have been left out in a contraction.

cannot = can't   will not = won't ← Some contractions don't quite match the words they're made from.

Apostrophes can also show possession. You usually add an apostrophe and an 's' to the end of a noun to show possession. If a noun is plural and ends in 's', you just add an apostrophe.

Imogen's skates   Nicholas's backpack   the butterflies' wings

The words 'its' and 'it's' mean two different things.

Its means 'belonging to it'. ⟶ The cat cleaned its paws.

It's means 'it is' or 'it has'. < It is heavy. = It's heavy.
It has broken. = It's broken.

Now Try These

1. Can you circle the mistake in each sentence below?
Then, rewrite the sentences without any mistakes.

Its time to give the cat its food. ⟹ ....

It's odd that my dog eats it's tail. ⟹ ....

It's lid is broken but it's fixable. ⟹ ....

It's such a shame that its closing. ⟹ ....

It's lovely that its been so sunny. ⟹ ....

2. Add two apostrophes where they are needed in each sentence below.

The boxes contents werent easy to unpack.

Ill try to go to Beatrices birthday party.

Jacobs bird flapped its wings but it couldnt fly.

Taika thinks his heads too big to fit in Ilas hat.

22

3. Rewrite each sentence below, turning two pairs of words into their contracted form.

I shall not keep these socks on as they are very itchy.

....

....

You must have heard that we are going to Japan next week.

....

....

4. Can you make the singular noun in each box plural? Then, write a sentence using each pair of nouns and an apostrophe to show possession.

child
kiwis
.... ➡ ....
....

fairy
prizes
.... ➡ ....
....

whale
cousins
.... ➡ ....
....

An Extra Challenge

Can you write two sentences to describe each of the pictures below? Each sentence should contain two apostrophes — one that shows possession and one that shows a contraction.

Do you have an appetite for apostrophes? Tick a box.

Direct speech

Direct speech is the words that someone says. Direct speech goes inside inverted commas and always begins with a capital letter.

He yelled, "Help me!"   "I'll try my best," she replied.

Put a comma before the speech starts.

You must end direct speech with a punctuation mark inside the inverted commas.

You don't need a capital letter here.

Direct speech can also be split into two parts.

"I hope," said Deidre, "that you look before you leap next time."

Add a comma here because the sentence hasn't finished.

Put a comma before the second bit of speech.

If the second bit of speech is part of the same sentence, you don't need a capital letter here.

Add a punctuation mark here because the sentence has ended.

Now Try These

1. Tick the sentences that are punctuated correctly.

   "Have you seen Dad?" I asked. ☐   "Look," Ella yelled, "I see the sea!" ☐

   "Wait," he said. Enofe isn't here." ☐   Marcus shouted "Watch out!" ☐

   "I'll come back later," she said ☐   "We swear it wasn't us," they lied. ☐

   Salma said, "I want ice cream." ☐   "Hello" she said, "I'm Cassandra." ☐

2. The sentences below use direct speech. Can you add the missing punctuation?

   April said I don't think I can go to the aquarium on Friday

   I should have won the prize he muttered under his breath

   Which should I buy asked Mary the green hat or the red one

   I'm right next to you explained Zac so you don't need to shout

24

3. Rewrite each sentence so that it uses direct speech broken up into two parts.

Grainne thinks she has lost her golf ball.

....

Matthew wondered if there would be pudding.

....

Mr Khan needs some flour to make a cake.

....

4. Can you write sentences that use direct speech and the words in each box?
   Make sure you put the direct speech in the place given in brackets.

| made   Khadija   orange | **(direct speech goes first)** |

....

| tiger   playground   Arthur | **(direct speech goes last)** |

....

| Muriel   yoga   weekend | **(direct speech in two parts)** |

....

An Extra Challenge

Here's part of a playscript.

Can you turn each line into a sentence that uses direct speech? Make sure you vary where you put the direct speech in each sentence.

Then, write five more sentences that use direct speech to continue the story.

MARIE:	Pass me that flask of purple liquid, please.
IULIA:	Of course, here you are Marie.
MARIE:	Thank you. This should be the final ingredient we need for our experiment.
IULIA:	How exciting! So many months of preparation have come down to this moment.
MARIE:	Let's hope that it has all been worth it...

"Now," I said, "it's time to tick a box to show how you got on."

Semi-colons, colons and dashes

How It Works

A semi-colon can be used instead of a conjunction to join two main clauses together. Each clause should be equally important and about the same thing.

I'm terrified of spiders; Dolores thinks they're cute.

↑

The semi-colon is used instead of the conjunction but.

Colons can be used to introduce explanations.
The part before the colon must always be a main clause.

Summer squealed loudly: her brother had startled her.

↗

This explains the main clause before the colon.

Single dashes can be used to separate two main clauses.

Leonard inspected his glasses — there was a crack in them.

Now Try These

1. Put a dash in the right box to complete each sentence below.

We missed ☐ our train ☐ to London ☐ we had overslept.

It happened again ☐ the parrot's ☐ singing ☐ woke me up.

Karen shouldn't ☐ have eaten ☐ so many sweets ☐ now she feels sick.

2. These sentences are punctuated incorrectly. Cross out the semi-colons that aren't needed.

Ducks; are my favourite animal; I really want; to get one; for my birthday this year.

Samuel doesn't like; chocolate cake; Eva happily ate his slice; for him.

I live; in England; my sister lives; thousands of miles away; in America.

I used to; have a pet cat; called Lord Pickles; he ran away; last year.

3. Add a colon in the right place in each sentence below.

You don't have to go to school Pratik it's Saturday today.

I have to mend my jeans my cat ripped a hole in the pocket.

Jared baked an apple pie for his nan it's her absolute favourite.

Alan didn't know what the huge present was it was a surprise.

4. Tick the sentences below where a semi-colon could be used instead of a conjunction.

Last year, I went to Paris <u>so</u> this year I'll go to Madrid. ☐

The seagulls cornered us <u>and</u> stole our fish and chips. ☐

Tomorrow, Adriene will either go bowling <u>or</u> lift weights. ☐

I checked the freezer <u>but</u> there was no vanilla ice cream. ☐

5. Complete each sentence with either a colon or a semi-colon.

They need to make camp soon .... it is starting to get dark.

Hetta went jet-skiing .... Penny sunbathed on the beach.

My legs felt like jelly .... we had been walking for hours.

Her aunt is from Austria .... her uncle is from Switzerland.

An Extra Challenge

Joanna has written a page of sentences but her dog has ripped it in half.

Can you complete each sentence by adding either a colon or a semi-colon and another clause?

Aunt Marjorie really likes daffodils and violets...

Neville is sewing a blanket out of old clothes...

I need to practise playing my clarinet tonight...

Sheldon bought an antique vase in France...

Tatsuo has three brothers and two sisters...

Stacey and Liang can't eat cheese any more...

Before you dash off, can you tick a box to show how you did?

 ☐ ☐ ☐

Punctuation in lists

How It Works

Colons can be used to introduce lists. The bit before the colon must always be a main clause.

> Josh has three goals: to look cool, to feel cool and to be cool.

You don't need to put a comma before the last item.

Semi-colons are used to separate long phrases or clauses in a list. You usually use them when there are other punctuation marks in the items of the list.

> I ate three huge, delicious cakes; two biscuits, both with chocolate chips; and a banana.

You need a semi-colon before the last item.

You can also write a list using bullet points. You can punctuate bullet points in different ways, but make sure you use the same punctuation throughout the list. For example:

I need:
- flour
- eggs
- butter

Use either capitals or lower case letters at the start of all the points.

For the match I need:
- Hockey stick,
- Shinpads,
- Sports kit.

You can use commas or semi-colons, with a full stop after the last point.

Now Try These

1. Tick the list which uses the right punctuation.

   I waved at: my older brother Leon, my cousin Abeo and my friend Natasha. ☐

   Tim needs to take some things to the picnic: a sandwich, an apple and a biscuit. ☐

   Mrs Jones said the test had three parts: spelling punctuation and grammar. ☐

2. Add colons or semi-colons in the right places in each list below.

   Saoirse has lots of stationery pens, pencils and highlighters.

   The cat was covered in glitter, which I had been using for a craft project feathers and sequins, which shone in the light.

   The dinner had three courses starter, main and pudding.

3. Write out the words and punctuation on the banners into full sentences.

a pug a spaniel and a poodle   . : ,   I have three dogs

....

singing pop songs   I love playing the piano particularly Mozart   ; . , ;   and rocking out on my guitar

....

....

4. Complete the list of animals in the picture. Make sure you use the right punctuation.

Several animals helped to hatch the escape plan:
- A white goat,

....

....

....

....

Chelsey has bought so many things for her party that she's lost track of what items she has.

Can you help her by writing a list of all the items below? First, write a list using commas. Then, rewrite your list using semi-colons. Finally, rewrite your list using bullet points.

Did this page go well, brilliantly or fantastically? Tick a box.

Suffixes

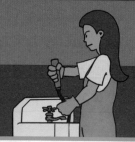

How It Works

A suffix is a letter or group of letters you add to the end of a root word to create a new word. Sometimes the spelling of the root word changes when a suffix is added. Here is an example:

mummy ✚ ify ➡ mummify ⟵ The 'y' in 'mummy' is removed when the suffix '-ify' is added.

root word   suffix   new word

Some words ending in '-fer' change their spelling when you add a suffix. If the '-fer' is emphasised when you say the new word out loud, you need to double the 'r'. For example:

prefer ✚ ing ➡ prefer<u>r</u>ing ⟵ '-fer' is emphasised when you say this word out loud, so an extra 'r' is added.

prefer ✚ ence ➡ preference ⟵ '-fer' is not emphasised when you say this word out loud, so the 'r' is not doubled.

Now Try These

1. Add either **-ise**, **-ate** or **-ify** to these root words to turn them into verbs.

final ➡ ....   fort ➡ ....

decor ➡ ....   equal ➡ ....

test ➡ ....   origin ➡ ....

2. Draw lines to match each root word to the right suffix. Then, write the completed words in the box. Be careful — the spelling of the root words might need to change.

beauty   affection   ise

glory   accuracy   ate

author   apology   ify

3. Each sentence below contains a spelling mistake. Underline the word with the wrong spelling, then rewrite it without any mistakes.

Fion kept refering to the weird event that happened last week.

....

I'm desparate to communicate instructions to my naughty dog.

....

Duong is absolutely terrorfied of creepy crawlies.

....

The football player was transfered to a better club.

....

Jazz didn't reallise that the teacher was watching.

....

4. Circle the words below that are spelt incorrectly. Then write some sentences using the words you've circled, spelt correctly. Use each word once.

memorise   simpleify

sufering   offerred   difference

....

....

....

An Extra Challenge

Tim was reading an article on his grandma's old computer, but it deleted some of the suffixes.

Can you rewrite the article, adding the correct suffixes so that Tim can understand it?

At the pie-eater of the year confer   , deb   over who should win had begun to intens   . Only three fortun   pie-eaters had reached the final, each of whom had just   their places by excelling in their specialisms — pork pies, apple pies and mud pies. After much confer   it was decided that the best way to pick the winner was to activ   their jaws one more time with a custard pie eating contest. The contenders would need to improv   — none of them had tackled custard before.

BZZAP!

Do you have great suffix tricks? Give a box a tick.

Word endings

FINISH

Some word endings sound similar, but are spelt differently.

For example, the 'unt' sound can be spelt in different ways.

innoc**ent**   observ**ant**

'-ent' is usually used after a soft 'c', soft 'g' or 'qu' sound.

If you can add '-ation' to a root word, e.g. 'observe' ('observation'), you usually need '-ant' not '-ent'.

Watch out, not all words follow these rules — sometimes you just need to learn the spellings.

Now Try These

1. Circle the right spelling of each word to complete the sentences below.

   The elephant is **considerably** / **consideribly** larger than expected.

   Hui thought that the history test was **impossible** / **impossable**.

   The **changable** / **changeable** weather in England annoys me.

   Sarah's writing was so messy it was almost **illegible** / **illegable**.

   There is a very **noticeable** / **noticible** jam stain on his jumper.

2. Circle the words that are spelt wrong. Then, write the incorrect words in the box without any mistakes.

hesitance

frequancy

decent

obediant

substence

confidence

independant

tolerence

accountant

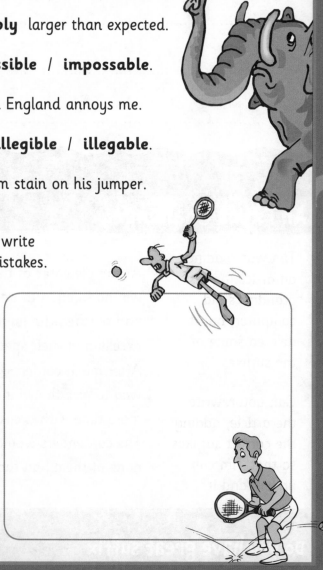

3. Use the root words from the box to complete the sentences below. You will need to change the spelling of the root words. You should only use each word once.

| influence   fiction   artifice   anxiety   province |

I'm ....ious that she'll think my accident was ....ious.

Scientists are making breakthroughs in ....ial intelligence.

The most ....ial factor in selecting our new dog was how cute it is.

Helen lives in a small, ...ial village, nestled amid the Alps.

4. Add a word ending from the box to each root word below.
Be careful — the spelling of the root word might need to change.
Then, write a sentence that uses each new word.

ant	tial
able	ent
cial	ible

assist ➕ .... ➡ ....

....

sense ➕ .... ➡ ....

....

finance ➕ .... ➡ ....

....

An Extra Challenge

Sir Wordendington has challenged you to a word ending duel. Write as many words as you can which contain the word endings below in order to claim victory. Make sure you spell the words correctly and don't use the words that are on these pages.

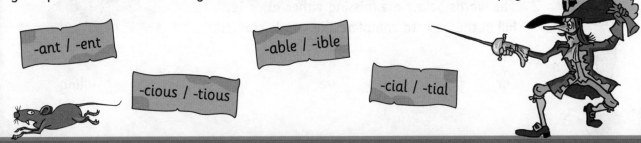

-ant / -ent

-cious / -tious

-able / -ible

-cial / -tial

Did you reach your potential on these pages? Tick a box.

33

Tricky words

How It Works

Watch out — some words are particularly tricky to spell.

ough**t** ← Some words contain sounds that aren't spelt as you would expect. In 'ought', the 'or' sound is spelt ough.

r**h**yme ← Some words contain silent letters that you can't hear when you say the word out loud.

prot**ei**n ← Some words don't follow spelling rules. 'protein' breaks the 'i' before 'e' rule.

Now Try These

1. Put a cross in the box next to the words that are spelt wrong.
   Then write the incorrect words in the box without any mistakes.

   furrow ☐   maintain ☐   drowt ☐   neyghbour ☐

   tuffer ☐   obeigh ☐   weight ☐   thoughtful ☐

2. The words below are missing either **ei** or **ie**.
   Fill in the gaps to complete the words correctly.

   gr.......f   dec.......ve   y.......ld   c.......ling

   h.......ght   anc.......nt   for.......gn   soc.......ty

34

3. Circle the words that are spelt wrong. Use the words you have circled to complete the sentences below, correcting the mistakes. Only use each word once.

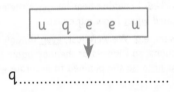

wrinkle   broose   glisten   equipped   fasen   definite

nowledge   amateur   vegtable   sutle   suggest   restling

The moral of the story was so .... that Anil completely missed it.

.... with Liv gave Fab a .... on his arm.

Olive has incredible .... of every type of ....

The man told us to .... our seatbelts as the ride was about to begin.

4. Rearrange each set of letters below to make a word. The first letter has been done for you. Then write three sentences using the words you've made — use each word once.

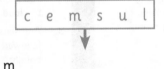

| u q e e u | c e m s u l | m a h s o t c |

q.................................   m.................................   s.................................

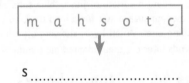

....

....

....

An Extra Challenge

Bill is building a wall out of tricky words, but he's not very good at spelling. Any mistakes will make the wall fall down. Can you help Bill by correcting the spelling mistakes?

vehikle	fisical	averige	embaras	orkward	critisice	relevent
familyar	develup	newsiance	soldjer	cureosity	acording	bargen
ocur	rythm	dictionery	interupt	privilige	identaty	profesion

Did you get the ~~riht ansers~~ right answers? Tick a box.

35

Answers

Pages 2-3 — Tenses

1. We <u>were</u> wondering who her hairdresser was. — past progressive / I <u>have</u> written a thrilling story about a snail. — present perfect / The car journey <u>had</u> been long and tiring. — past perfect / Jemima <u>is</u> riding her horse called Matilda. — present progressive

2. Leila <u>has given</u> cards to her friends. / The explorers <u>had sailed</u> across the ocean. / Evan <u>is talking</u> to the zoo keeper. / I <u>was dancing</u> around the room with joy.

3. Sonja <u>had hoped</u> to become a pirate. / The superhero <u>was flying</u> around the rooftops. / They <u>are uncovering</u> an ancient city beneath the sand. / The magician <u>has lifted</u> the table with a spell.

4. Any suitable sentences, e.g. Present progressive: The chicken is riding a bicycle. / Past perfect: The chicken had stunned everyone by doing tricks on its bicycle.

An Extra Challenge

Dear Diary, Today, while my brothers <u>were</u> browsing the bookshop, I was <u>trying</u> on clothes at the new shop in town. I had <u>wanted</u> to visit since it opened. I noticed that the shop <u>was</u> selling a variety of fancy, blue suits. I have <u>dreamt</u> of owning such a suit for a long time, so I was thinking of buying one. When I <u>was</u> showing off my new suit to my friends later on, they admired my trendy new look.

Pages 4-5 — Noun phrases

1. Any sensible answers, e.g. He finally spotted the <u>tropical</u> coastline of the small island. / Vinodh asked the tall, <u>cheerful</u> man behind the counter a question. / She lives in a strange, futuristic house <u>outside</u> the town centre. / I donated an enormous stack of <u>novels</u> to the charity shop.

2. Any sensible expanded noun phrases that include the words in the box, e.g. the incredibly annoying boy at the nearby funfair / a very friendly mole on a sandy beach

3. You should have underlined: the adorable baby elephants at the zoo / a glass of freshly-squeezed orange juice
Any noun phrases that make sense in the sentences.

4. Any sensible noun phrases where words have been added before and after the nouns, e.g. The <u>affectionate toddler with brown hair</u> cuddled <u>her fluffy dog sitting in the kitchen</u> and <u>a friendly cat from the neighbour's garden</u>.

An Extra Challenge

Any five sensible expanded noun phrases.

Pages 6-7 — Clauses

1. You should have ticked: The milk in the tea <u>that I'm drinking</u> doesn't taste fresh. / That summer <u>we spent surfing at the beach</u> was fun.

2. Any sensible relative clauses, e.g. John, <u>who was adventurous</u>, explored the ruins. / We opened the door, <u>which creaked noisily</u>, and peeked inside. / My house is on a hill <u>that is incredibly steep</u>. / I looked at the sky <u>which was grey and gloomy</u>. / Lucy, <u>whose hair was very long</u>, wanted a haircut.

3. Any sensible answers, e.g. I rode my bike to school <u>because it was a lovely day</u>. / <u>Unless you concentrate</u>, the spell won't work. / We can go jet-skiing <u>once we've finished our homework</u>.

4. Any sensible sentences that contain the words from the box,

a main clause and a relative clause, e.g. I am excited to see the band, whose music I love, perform in my town. / The lightning, that was very bright, hurt my eyes.

An Extra Challenge

I had a tennis lesson, which ended in a match with Fred. I hit the ball so hard his racket broke! We played until we were exhausted. Then we ate some cake, which we felt was well deserved. In order to cool off, we had a water fight.

There are five main clauses. (I had a tennis lesson / I hit the ball so hard / We played / Then we ate some cake / we had a water fight)

Pages 8-9 — Conjunctions

1. <u>Whenever</u> Danny sees a tree, he can't resist climbing it. / George thanked them many times, <u>for</u> he was extremely grateful. / <u>Provided that</u> there are enough seats on the spaceship, you can all come along. / We promise not to leave <u>until</u> you are ready. / <u>Though</u> the cheese is delicious, I won't have any more.

2. You should have underlined: since, but, when, so
You should have ticked: I couldn't hear her <u>since</u> the music was too loud. / I screamed <u>when</u> I saw my haircut.

3. Any sensible answers, e.g. We were lost, <u>even though</u> I had followed the directions, <u>so</u> I looked at the map again. / Alice bought some paint <u>because</u> she planned to decorate <u>when</u> she moved house.

4. Any sensible answers, e.g. He's been learning karate <u>since</u> he was a young boy. / They can't open the chest <u>unless</u> they find the key. / <u>Although</u> it wasn't allowed, Kyle stood on the chair.

An Extra Challenge

Any sensible sentences that each use at least one conjunction.

Pages 10-11 — Adverbials

1. <u>Every so often</u>, I buy sweets with my pocket money. / Karim likes potatoes. <u>In contrast</u>, I despise them. / The teacher told us we had to sit <u>very quietly</u>.

2. We decided to go home <u>as soon as possible</u>. — when
Josie practises the guitar <u>once or twice a day</u>. — how often
<u>With extreme caution</u>, Pandora lifted the lid. — how
I think that I left my homework <u>on the bus</u>. — where

3. Any sensible adverbials that match the headings, e.g.

	when	where	how	how often
I run.	I run <u>after school</u>.	I run <u>to the supermarket</u>.	I run <u>as slowly as a snail</u>.	I run <u>every single day</u>.
Elsa shouted.	Elsa shouted <u>until dinnertime</u>.	Elsa shouted <u>in the playground</u>.	Elsa shouted <u>at the top of her voice</u>.	Elsa shouted <u>once in her entire life</u>.

4. Any sensible sentences, e.g. My cousins live <u>down the road</u>. / They sleep through their alarms <u>most mornings</u>. / <u>With increasing panic</u>, Ahmed looked for his keys.

An Extra Challenge

Any sensible descriptions, using adverbials to show where, when and how each event happens.

Pages 12-13 — Subject and object

1. You should have underlined: The cat, Bert, The policeman, I, The friendly robot, Paul, Noah, My teacher.
You should have circled: the cream, the precious vase, her, the

Answers

grape, her arm, the sweet, his pet duck, me

2. stroked — verb / The unicorn — subject / The dog — subject / his basket — object / emailed — verb

3. Any sensible choice of subject or object.

4. Any sensible sentences that describe the pictures, where the subject is underlined and the object is circled.

An Extra Challenge

Any five sensible sentences that each use one of the subjects, one of the verbs and an object. The subjects are: Chidima, the brave mouse, the chickens, Raphaelle, the shy child
The verbs are: ate, scared, greeted, heaved, painted

Pages 14-15 — Passive and active

1. My brother played video games all afternoon. — A / Clarisse was chased by a swarm of angry bees. — P / The gold medals were awarded by the judges. — P / The plant doubled in size within a single week. — A / The party was organised by Patrick's mother. — P

2. You should have ticked: The goal was scored by Carlos. / The card was made by my aunt.
Carlos scored the goal. / My aunt made the card.

3. The flamingo was scared by the hippo. / My favourite mug was smashed by Riya. / The tree was blown over by the storm.

4. You should have ticked: Mia was given a kitten. / The cake was baked. <u>Obasi</u> — subject, <u>Mia</u> — subject, <u>the quiz</u> — object, <u>The cake</u> — subject

An Extra Challenge

Any sensible answer, e.g. The head of Space Pets, Colonel Kitten, gave Doug and Kat their top secret mission. First, the Colonel asked them to locate the wicked alien. Then, he instructed them to send the alien back to its home planet. "What if the alien overpowers us, and evil forces conquer the galaxy?" Kat asked — the scale of the mission alarmed her. However, Doug reassured her.
"Space Pets awarded us the top prize last year. We can do this," he barked. "Let's go!" And so they fired up their jet packs and started the top secret mission.

Pages 16-17 — Formal and informal writing

1. The chippy's brill, isn't it? — The chip shop is brilliant. / I hang out with my mates. — I spend time with my friends. / If I'd wanted to, I could've left. — If I were so inclined, I could have left.

2. The <u>kids</u> were playing inside. — I / Jan <u>ditched</u> me outside the zoo. — I / I <u>informed</u> her about the test. — F / Max <u>requested</u> to leave the room. — F / It was really enjoyable, <u>wasn't it?</u> — I / <u>Had I gone</u>, I would have had fun. — F

3. Catherine was dead <u>chuffed</u> about winning the race, wasn't she? / Khushi was <u>busted</u> when her dad saw her munching the sweets. / Were she to do something wrong, she would be <u>apprehended</u>. / I was extremely <u>elated</u> about the outcome of the experiment.

4. Hand me the grub — I'm starving. — I / My mother instructed Zara to relax. — F / If I'd made a joke, she would've cracked up. — I
Any sensible rewrites, e.g. Pass me the food please — I am hungry. / My mum told Zara to chill out. / Had I made a joke,

she would have laughed.

An Extra Challenge

Any sensible rewrites that make the note to Kim's dad informal and the letter of complaint formal.

Pages 18-19 — Quizzical quest

1. passive — A
2. informal — L
3. 2 (It's, can't) — A
4. subject — C
5. present perfect — K

6. since — A
7. affluent — Z
8. no — A
9. demolish — M
10. all through the night — O

The magic word is: ALACKAZAMO

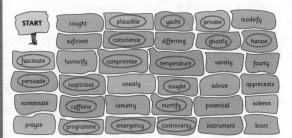

Pages 20-21 — Synonyms and antonyms

1. There was a moment of <u>quiet</u> before the storm hit. — peace / He <u>softly</u> stroked the puppy behind its ears. — gently / There was a brief <u>pause</u> in the conversation. — lull / The lizard moved <u>sneakily</u> across the glass. — stealthily

2. always — adverb, harmless — adjective, enemy — noun punished — verb, mean — adjective
Any antonyms, e.g. never, harmful, friend, rewarded, kind

3. Any synonyms, e.g. joyful / helping / pretty / concentrated

4. Any antonyms, e.g. Emeka <u>tightly</u> wrapped himself up in the <u>soft</u> blanket. / In <u>winter</u>, the nights are <u>longer</u> and the days are <u>cooler</u>. / She <u>accepted</u> the invitation because it sounded <u>fun</u>. / <u>Nobody</u> was happy about the mission's <u>failure</u>.

An Extra Challenge

fre<u>qu</u>ently, <u>ch</u>uckle, persua<u>d</u>e, f<u>r</u>ail, certa<u>i</u>nly, ang<u>e</u>r, timi<u>d</u>ly — the unscrambled letters spell 'decline'
Any sensible sentence that uses an antonym of decline.

Pages 22-23 — Apostrophes

1. <u>It's</u> time to give the cat its food. / It's odd that my dog eats <u>its</u> tail. / <u>Its</u> lid is broken but it's fixable. / It's such a shame that <u>it's</u> closing. / It's lovely that <u>it's</u> been so sunny.

2. The boxes' contents weren't easy to unpack. / I'll try to go to Beatrice's birthday party. / Jacob's bird flapped its wings but it couldn't fly. / Taika thinks his head's too big to fit in Ila's hat.

3. I <u>shan't</u> keep these socks on as <u>they're</u> very itchy. / You <u>must've</u> heard that <u>we're</u> going to Japan next week.

4. children, fairies, whales
Any sensible sentences, e.g. The children's kiwis had happy faces drawn on them. / I was honoured to distribute the fairies' prizes. / There had been a fight between the whales' cousins.

An Extra Challenge

Any sensible sentences about the pictures which contain an apostrophe to show possession and a contraction.

Answers

Pages 24-25 — Direct speech

1. You should have ticked: "Have you seen Dad?" I asked. / Salma said, "I want ice cream." / "Look," Ella yelled, "I see the sea!" / "We swear it wasn't us," they lied.

2. April said, "I don't think I can go to the aquarium on Friday." / "I should have won the prize," he muttered under his breath. / "Which should I buy," asked Mary, "the green hat or the red one?" / "I'm right next to you," explained Zac, "so you don't need to shout."

3. Any sensible sentences, e.g. "I think," exclaimed Grainne, "that I've lost my golf ball." / "I wonder," pondered Matthew, "if there will be pudding." / "I need some flour," said Mr Khan, "to make a cake."

4. Any sensible sentences, e.g. "I have made some orange jelly," said Khadija. / Arthur explained, "The tiger was found in the playground." / "At the weekend," said Muriel, "I'll do yoga."

An Extra Challenge

Any sensible sentences that use direct speech correctly in different parts of the sentence, followed by five sensible sentences that use direct speech correctly and continue the story.

Pages 26-27 — Semi-colons, colons and dashes

1. We missed our train to London — we had overslept. / It happened again — the parrot's singing woke me up. / Karen shouldn't have eaten so many sweets — now she feels sick.

2. Ducks are my favourite animal; I really want to get one for my birthday this year. / Samuel doesn't like chocolate cake; Eva happily ate his slice for him. / I live in England; my sister lives thousands of miles away in America. / I used to have a pet cat called Lord Pickles; he ran away last year.

3. You don't have to go to school Pratik: it's Saturday today. / I have to mend my jeans: my cat ripped a hole in the pocket. / Jared baked an apple pie for his nan: it's her absolute favourite. / Alan didn't know what the huge present was: it was a surprise.

4. You should have ticked: Last year I went to Paris so this year I'll go to Madrid. / I checked the freezer but there was no vanilla ice cream.

5. They need to make camp soon: it is starting to get dark. / Hetta went jet skiing; Penny sunbathed on the beach. / My legs felt like jelly: we had been walking for hours. / Her aunt is from Austria; her uncle is from Switzerland.

An Extra Challenge

Any sensible clauses that complete the sentences and use a semi-colon or colon correctly.

Pages 28-29 — Punctuation in lists

1. You should have ticked: Tim needs to take some things to the picnic: a sandwich, an apple and a biscuit.

2. Saoirse has lots of stationery: pens, pencils and highlighters. / The cat was covered in glitter, which I had been using for a craft project; feathers; and sequins, which shone in the light. / The dinner had three courses: starter, main and pudding.

3. I have three dogs: a pug, a spaniel and a poodle. / I love playing the piano, particularly Mozart; singing pop songs; and

rocking out on my guitar.

4. Any sensible list that is punctuated correctly. Each bullet point should start with a capital letter and end with a comma, except the last bullet point, which should end with a full stop.

An Extra Challenge

Any lists that are punctuated correctly and include all the items.

Pages 30-31 — Suffixes

1. finalise, decorate, testify, fortify, equalise, originate

2. authorise, apologise, affectionate, accurate, beautify, glorify

3. referring / desperate / terrified / transferred / realise

4. You should have circled: sufering, offerred, simpleify
   Any sensible sentences that use these words.

An Extra Challenge

conference, debate, intensify, fortunate, justified, conferring, activate, improvise

Pages 32-33 — Word endings

1. The elephant is considerably larger than expected. / Hui thought that the history test was impossible. / The changeable weather in England annoys me. / Sarah's writing was so messy it was almost illegible. / There is a very noticeable jam stain on his jumper.

2. You should have circled: frequancy, obediant, substence, independant, tolerence
   You should have written: frequency, obedient, substance, independent, tolerance

3. I'm anxious that she'll think my accident was fictitious. / Scientists are making breakthroughs in artificial intelligence. / The most influential factor in selecting our new dog was how cute it is. / Helen lives in a small, provincial village, nestled amid the Alps.

4. assist + ant — assistant / sense + ible — sensible / finance + cial — financial
   Any sensible sentences that use the new words.

An Extra Challenge

Any words that contain the endings and are spelt correctly.

Pages 34-35 — Tricky words

1. You should have crossed: drowt, neyghbour, tuffer, obeigh
   You should have written: drought, neighbour, tougher, obey

2. grief, deceive, yield, ceiling, height, ancient, foreign, society

3. You should have circled: broose, fasen, nowledge, vegtable, sutle, restling
   The moral of the story was so subtle that Anil completely missed it. / Wrestling with Liv gave Fab a bruise on his arm. / Olive has incredible knowledge of every type of vegetable. / The man told us to fasten our seatbelts as the ride was about to begin.

4. queue, muscle, stomach
   Any sensible sentences that use these words.

An Extra Challenge

The correct spellings are: vehicle, physical, average, embarrass, awkward, criticise, relevant, familiar, develop, nuisance, soldier, curiosity, according, bargain, occur, rhythm, dictionary, interrupt, privilege, identity, profession

EPE6GO21